Chemistry for the Grammar Stage

Student Workbook

Chemistry for the Grammar Stage Student Workbook

Updated Edition (Third Printing 2020)
Copyright @ Elemental Science, Inc.
Email: support@elementalscience.com

ISBN # 978-1-935614-49-4

Printed in the USA for worldwide distribution

For more copies write to:
Elemental Science
PO Box 79
Niceville, FL 32588
support@elementalscience.com

Copyright Policy

Chemistry for the Grammar Stage Student Workbook

Chemistry for the Grammar Stage

Atoms and Molecules Unit

Atoms and Molecules Poster

Subatomic Particles

Atoms and Elements

Molecules and Compounds

e- p+

n

Subatomic Particles

Atoms

Isotopes

$$\begin{array}{|c|}\hline 17 \\ \mathbf{Cl}_{18n} \\ \text{Chlorine} \\ 35 \\ \hline \end{array}$$

$$\begin{array}{|c|}\hline 17 \\ \mathbf{Cl}_{20n} \\ \text{Chlorine} \\ 37 \\ \hline \end{array}$$

Chemistry for the Grammar Stage Student Workbook ~ Atoms and Molecules Unit Week 1

Lab Report: Model Atom

Our Tools

_____   _____

_____   _____

Our Method

_____

_____

_____

_____

Our Outcome

My Model

Our Insight

_____

_____

_____

Electron Shells

_____ electrons fit in the first shell.

_____ electrons fit in the second shell.

_____ electrons fit in the third shell.

Molecules

_____

_____

_____

_____

_____

_____

Polar and Nonpolar

_____

_____

_____

_____

_____

_____

_____

_____

Lab Report: Molecule Mixture

Our Tools

_____   _____

_____   _____

_____   _____

Our Method

_____

_____

_____

Our Outcome

First Observation	After 24 Hours

12

Air

_____

_____

_____

_____

_____

_____

_____

Oxygen

_____

_____

_____

_____

_____

_____

8
O
Oxygen
15.999

Carbon Dioxide

_____

_____

_____

_____

_____

_____

Lab Report: An Empty Sack

Our Tools

_____   _____

_____   _____

Our Method

What it looked like

_____

_____

_____

_____

_____

_____

_____

_____

_____

_____

Our Outcome

_____

_____

_____

_____

Our Insight

_____

_____

_____

14

Water

_____

_____

_____

_____

_____

_____

_____

Water as a Solvent

_____

_____

_____

_____

_____

_____

_____

Hard Water

_____

_____

_____

_____

_____

_____

_____

Lab Report: Disappearing Salt

Our Tools

_____   _____

_____   _____

Our Method

┌─────────────────────────┐
│   What it looked like   │
│   │
│   │
│   │
│   │
│   │
│   │
│   │
│   │
└─────────────────────────┘

_____

_____

_____

_____

_____

_____

_____

_____

Our Outcome

_____

_____

_____

_____

Our Insight

_____

_____

_____

Chemistry for the Grammar Stage

Periodic Table Unit

18

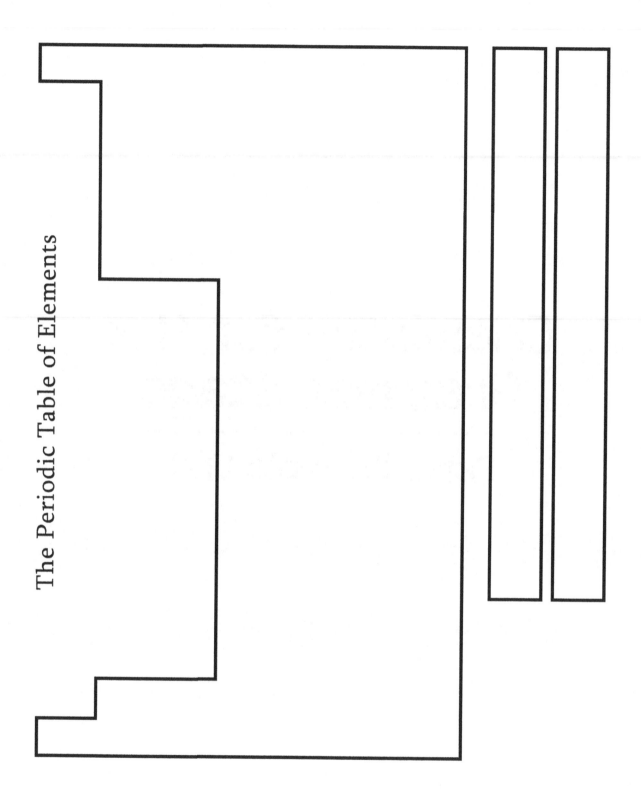

The Periodic Table of Elements

Chemistry for the Grammar Stage Student Workbook ~ Periodic Table Unit Project

8
O
Oxygen
15.999

Elements

_____
_____
_____
_____
_____
_____
_____
_____
_____

_____
_____

Periodic Table

- -
- -
- -
- -
- -
- -
- -
- -
- -

Lab Report: Table Sorting

Our Tools

_____   _____

_____   _____

Our Outcome

My Table

Our Insight

_____

_____

_____

1
H
Hydrogen
1.008

3
Li
Lithium
6.041

11
Na
Sodium
22.99

19
K
Potassium
39.1

37
Rb
Rubidium
85.47

55
Cs
Cesium
132.9

87
Fr
Francium
223

Alkali Metals

_____

_____

_____

_____

_____

_____

Hydrogen

_____

_____

_____

_____

_____

Sodium

_____

_____

_____

_____

_____

Lab Report: Colder Water

Our Tools

_____   _____

_____   _____

_____   _____

Our Method

What it looked like

_____
_____
_____
_____
_____
_____
_____
_____
_____

Our Outcome

_____
_____
_____

Our Insight

_____

11
Na
Sodium
22.99

_____

_____

4
Be
Beryllium
9.012
12
Mg
Magnesium
24.3
20
Ca
Calcium
40.08
38
Sr
Strontium
87.62
56
Ba
Barium
137.3
88
Ra
Radium
226

Alkaline Earth Metals

_____

_____

_____

_____

_____

_____

_____

Magnesium

_____

_____

_____

_____

_____

_____

Calcium

_____

_____

_____

_____

_____

_____

Lab Report: Magnesium Milk

Our Tools

_____   _____

_____   _____

_____   _____

Our Method

What it looked like

Our Outcome

Our Insight

12
Mg
Magnesium
24.3

Transition Metals

_____

_____

_____

_____

21	22	23	24	25	26	27	28	29	30
Sc	**Ti**	**V**	**Cr**	**Mn**	**Fe**	**Co**	**Ni**	**Cu**	**Zn**
Scandium	Titanium	Vanadium	Chromium	Manganese	Iron	Cobalt	Nickel	Copper	Zinc
44.96	47.87	50.94	52	54.94	55.85	58.93	58.69	63.55	65.39
39	40	41	42	43	44	45	46	47	48
Y	**Zr**	**Nb**	**Mo**	**Tc**	**Ru**	**Rh**	**Pd**	**Ag**	**Cd**
Yttrium	Zirconium	Niobium	Molybdenum	Technetium	Ruthenium	Rhodium	Palladium	Silver	Cadmium
88.91	91.22	92.91	95.94	98.91	101.07	102.91	106.42	107.87	112.41
* 71	72	73	74	75	76	77	78	79	80
Lu	**Hf**	**Ta**	**W**	**Re**	**Os**	**Ir**	**Pt**	**Au**	**Hg**
Lutetium	Hafnium	Tantalum	Tungsten	Rhenium	Osmium	Iridium	Platinum	Gold	Mercury
175	178.49	180.95	183.85	186.21	190.2	192.2	195.08	196.97	200.59
** 103	104	105	106	107	108	109	110	111	112
Lr	**Rf**	**Db**	**Sg**	**Bh**	**Hs**	**Mt**	**Ds**	**Rg**	**Cn**
Lawrencium	Rutherfordium	Dubnium	Seaborgium	Bohrium	Hassium	Meitnerium	Darmstadtium	Roentgenium	Copernicium
262	261.11	262.11	263.12	264.1	265.1	266	[271]	[272]	[277]

Iron

_____

_____

_____

_____

Copper

_____

_____

_____

_____

Lab Report: Drinkable Iron

Our Tools

_____   _____

_____   _____

_____   _____

Our Method

_____

_____

_____

_____

_____

Our Outcome

Type of Juice	Presence of Iron after 20 minutes	Presence of Iron after 2 hours

Our Insight

_____

_____

_____

_____

26
Fe
Iron
55.85

5
B
Boron
10.81
13
Al
Aluminum
26.98
31
Ga
Gallium
69.72
49
In
Indium
114.82
81
Tl
Thallium
204.38
113
Nh
Nihonium

Boron Elements

_____

_____

_____

_____

_____

_____

_____

Boron

_____

_____

_____

_____

_____

_____

Aluminum

_____

_____

_____

_____

_____

_____

Lab Report: Sinking Gel

Our Tools

_____   _____

_____   _____

_____   _____

Our Method

What it looked like

_____
_____
_____
_____
_____
_____
_____
_____
_____
_____

Our Outcome

_____
_____
_____
_____

Our Insight

_____
_____
_____

| 13 |
| Al |
| Aluminum |
| 26.98 |

6
C
Carbon
12.01
14
Si
Silicon
28.09
32
Ge
Germanium
72.61
50
Sn
Tin
118.71
82
Pb
Lead
207.2
114
Fl
Flerovium

Carbon Elements

_____

_____

_____

_____

_____

_____

Carbon

_____

_____

_____

_____

_____

_____

Tin

_____

_____

_____

_____

_____

_____

Lab Report: Chemical Breath

Our Tools

_____   _____

_____   _____

_____   _____

Our Method

What it looked like

_____

_____

_____

_____

_____

_____

_____

_____

_____

Our Outcome

_____

_____

_____

_____

Our Insight

_____

_____

_____

6
C
Carbon
12.01

7
N
Nitrogen
14.01

15
P
Phosphorus
30.97

33
As
Arsenic
74.92

51
Sb
Antimony
121.76

83
Bi
Bismuth
208.98

115
Mc
Moscovium

Nitrogen Elements

_____

_____

_____

_____

_____

_____

Nitrogen

_____

_____

_____

_____

_____

_____

Phosphorus

_____

_____

_____

_____

_____

_____

Lab Report: Shiny Pennies

Our Tools

_____   _____

_____   _____

_____   _____

Our Method

_____

_____

_____

_____

Our Outcome

Before	After

Our Insight

_____

_____

_____

_____

| 15 |
| **P** |
| Phosphorus |
| 30.97 |

8
O
Oxygen
16
16
S
Sulfur
32.07
34
Se
Selenium
78.96
52
Te
Tellurium
127.6
84
Po
Polonium
208.98
116
Lv
Livermorium

Oxygen Elements

_____

_____

_____

_____

_____

_____

_____

Oxygen

_____

_____

_____

_____

_____

_____

Sulfur

_____

_____

_____

_____

_____

_____

Lab Report: Browning Apple

Our Tools

_____   _____

_____   _____

_____   _____

Our Method

_____

_____

_____

_____

Our Outcome

Without Vitamin C	With Vitamin C

Our Insight

_____

_____

_____

_____

| 8 |
| O |
| Oxygen |
| 15.999 |

9 **F** Fluorine 19	**Halogens** _____ _____ _____ _____ _____ _____
17 **Cl** Chlorine 35.45	
35 **Br** Bromine 79.9	**Fluorine** _____ _____ _____ _____ _____ _____
53 **I** Iodine 126.9	
85 **At** Astatine 209.9	**Iodine** _____ _____ _____ _____ _____ _____ _____
117 **Ts** Tennessine	

Lab Report: Magic Writing

Our Tools

_____   _____

_____   _____

_____   _____

Our Method

_____

_____

_____

_____

Our Outcome

Glue your message here.

53
I
Iodine
126.9

Our Insight

_____

_____

_____

2
He
Helium
4
10
Ne
Neon
20.18
18
Ar
Argon
39.95
36
Kr
Krypton
83.8
54
Xe
Xenon
131.29
86
Rn
Radon
222.02
118
Og
Oganesson

Noble Gases

_____

_____

_____

_____

_____

_____

Helium

_____

_____

_____

_____

_____

Neon

_____

_____

_____

_____

_____

Lab Report: Funny Voice

Our Tools

_____   _____

_____   _____

_____   _____

Our Method

_____

_____

_____

_____

_____

Our Outcome

_____

_____

_____

_____

_____

Our Insight

_____

_____

_____

_____

| 2 |
| **He** |
| Helium |
| 4 |

Lanthanides

_____

_____

_____

_____

_____

57	58	59	60	61	62	63	64	65	66	67	68	69	70
La	**Ce**	**Pr**	**Nd**	**Pm**	**Sm**	**Eu**	**Gd**	**Tb**	**Dy**	**Ho**	**Er**	**Tm**	**Yb**
Lanthanum	Cerium	Praseodymium	Neodymium	Promethium	Samarium	Europium	Gadolinium	Terbium	Dysprosium	Holmium	Erbium	Thulium	Ytterbium
138.91	140.12	14.91	144.24	144.91	150.36	151.96	157.25	158.93	162.5	164.93	167.26	168.93	173.04

Lanthanum

_____

_____

_____

_____

_____

57

La

Lanthanum

138.91

60

Nd

Neodymium

144.24

Neodymium

_____

_____

_____

_____

_____

_____

Lab Report: Moving Pencils

Our Tools

_____   _____

_____   _____

_____   _____

Our Method

_____

_____

_____

_____

Our Outcome

What it looked like

Our Insight

_____

_____

_____

57
La
Lanthanum
138.91

Actindes

_____
_____
_____
_____
_____

89	90	91	92	93	94	95	96	97	98	99	100	101	102
Ac	**Th**	**Pa**	**U**	**Np**	**Pu**	**Am**	**Cm**	**Bk**	**Cf**	**Es**	**Fm**	**Md**	**No**
Actinium	Thorium	Protactinium	Uranium	Neptunium	Plutonium	Americium	Curium	Berkelium	Californium	Einsteinium	Fermium	Mendelevium	Nobelium
227.03	232.04	231.04	238.03	237.04	244.06	243.06	247.07	247.07	251.08	252.08	257.1	258.1	259.1

Uranium

_____
_____
_____
_____
_____

92

U

Uranium
238.03

95

Am

Americium
243.06

Americium

_____
_____
_____
_____
_____
_____

Lab Report: Half-life

Our Tools

_____   _____

_____   _____

_____   _____

Our Method

_____

_____

_____

_____

_____

Our Outcome

_____

_____

_____

Our Insight

_____

_____

_____

_____

89	90	91	92	93	94	95	96	97	98	99	100	101	102
Ac	**Th**	**Pa**	**U**	**Np**	**Pu**	**Am**	**Cm**	**Bk**	**Cf**	**Es**	**Fm**	**Md**	**No**
Actinium	Thorium	Protactinium	Uranium	Neptunium	Plutonium	Americium	Curium	Berkelium	Californium	Einsteinium	Fermium	Mendelevium	Nobelium
227.03	232.04	231.04	238.03	237.04	244.06	243.06	247.07	247.07	251.08	252.08	257.1	258.1	259.1

Chemistry for the Grammar Stage

Physical Changes Unit

States of Matter Poster

Gases

Liquids

Solids

48

Solid

_____

_____

_____

_____

_____

_____

_____

Liquid

_____

_____

_____

_____

_____

_____

_____

Gas

_____

_____

_____

_____

_____

_____

_____

Lab Report: Playing with Matter

Our Tools

_____   _____

_____   _____

Our Method

_____

_____

_____

_____

Our Outcome

	My Observations
Balloon with Ice	
Balloon with Water	
Balloon with Air	

Our Insight

_____

_____

_____

Changes in State

Melting

Freezing

_____

_____

_____

_____

Boiling

Condensing

_____

_____

_____

_____

Lab Report: Freezy Meltdown

Our Tools

_____   _____

_____   _____

Our Method

_____

_____

_____

_____

Our Outcome

	My Observations
Juice (At the beginning)	
Juice (After time in freezer)	
Juice (After time on the counter)	

Our Insight

_____

_____

_____

How Liquids Behave

_____
_____
_____
_____
_____
_____
_____
_____

Evaporation

_____
_____
_____
_____
_____
_____
_____

Surface Tension

_____
_____
_____
_____
_____
_____
_____

Chemistry for the Grammar Stage Student Workbook ~ Physical Changes Unit Week 3

Lab Report: Floating Sticks

Our Tools

_____   _____

_____   _____

Our Method

┌─────────────────────┐
│ What it looked like │
│   │
└─────────────────────┘

Our Outcome

Our Insight

54

Brownian Motion

_____

_____

_____

_____

_____

_____

_____

Diffusion

_____

_____

_____

_____

_____

_____

_____

Open
Valve

Pressure and Temperature

_____

_____

_____

_____

_____

_____

Lab Report: Clicking Coin

Our Tools

_____   _____

_____   _____

Our Method

┌─────────────────────────────┐
│   **What it looked like**   │   _____
│   │   _____
│   │   _____
│   │   _____
│   │   _____
│   │   _____
│   │   _____
│   │   _____
│   │   _____
│   │   _____
└─────────────────────────────┘   _____

Our Outcome

_____

_____

_____

_____

Our Insight

_____

_____

_____

_____

Chemistry for the Grammar Stage

Chemical Changes Unit

Chemical Changes Poster

Metallic bonding

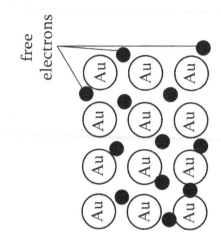

Covalent bonding

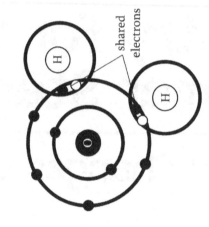

Ionic Bonding

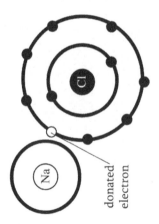

HCl + NaOH ⟶ H$_2$O + NaCl

Exothermic / Endothermic

Oxidation / Reduction

60

Ionic bonding

donated electron

_____
_____
_____
_____
_____
_____
_____

Covalent bonding

_____
_____
_____
_____
_____
_____
_____

shared electrons

Metallic bonding

free electrons

_____
_____
_____
_____
_____
_____

Chemistry for the Grammar Stage Student Workbook ~ Chemical Changes Unit Week 1

Lab Report: Moving Drop

Our Tools

_____   _____

_____   _____

Our Method

┌─────────────────────────────┐
│   **What it looked like**   │   _____
│   │   _____
│   │   _____
│   │   _____
│   │   _____
│   │   _____
│   │   _____
│   │   _____
│   │   _____
└─────────────────────────────┘

Our Outcome

_____

_____

_____

_____

Our Insight

additional
electron

_____

_____

_____

_____

Chemical Reactions

_____

_____

_____

_____

_____

_____

Conservation of Mass

$$HCl + NaOH \longrightarrow H_2O + NaCl$$

_____

_____

_____

_____

Moles

$$6.023 \times 10^{23}$$

_____

_____

_____

_____

_____

_____

Lab Report: Green Pennies

Our Tools

_____   _____

_____   _____

Our Method

┌─────────────────────────────┐
│   What it looked like   │   _____
│   │   _____
│   │   _____
│   │   _____
│   │   _____
│   │   _____
│   │   _____
│   │   _____
│   │   _____
└─────────────────────────────┘   _____

Our Outcome

_____

_____

_____

_____

Our Insight

_____

_____

_____

_____

Types of Reaction

_____

_____

_____

_____

_____

_____

_____

_____

_____

_____

_____

_____

Catalysts and Enzymes

_____

_____

_____

_____

_____

_____

_____

_____

_____

_____

_____

Lab Report: Chemical Reactions in your Mouth

Our Tools

_____   _____

_____   _____

Our Method

_____

_____

_____

_____

_____

Our Outcome

Type of Bread	Color of Reaction
Plain Bread	
Chewed-up Bread	

Our Insight

_____

_____

_____

_____

66

Oxidation

_____

_____

_____

_____

_____

_____

_____

_____

_____

_____

_____

Reduction

_____

_____

_____

_____

_____

_____

_____

_____

_____

_____

_____

Lab Report: Browning

Our Tools

_____   _____

_____   _____

Our Method

_____

_____

_____

_____

_____

Our Outcome

Time	Plain Apple Half	Apple Half with Lemon Juice
After 1 hour		
After 2 hours		
After 3 hours		
After 4 hours		

Our Insight

_____

_____

_____

Chemistry for the Grammar Stage

Mixtures Unit

Mixture Poster

Separating Mixtures

Filtration   Chromatography   Distillation

Crystals

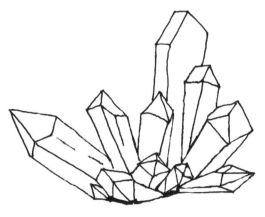

Mixtures

_____

_____

_____

_____

_____

_____

_____

_____

_____

_____

_____

Mixing Liquids

_____

_____

_____

_____

_____

_____

_____

_____

_____

_____

_____

Lab Report: Streamers of Color

Our Tools

_____   _____

_____   _____

Our Method

┌─────────────────────────┐
│ What it looked like
│
│
│
│
│
│
│
│
│
│
└─────────────────────────┘

_____
_____
_____
_____
_____
_____
_____
_____
_____

Our Outcome

_____
_____
_____
_____

Our Insight

_____
_____
_____
_____

Filtration

_____

_____

_____

_____

_____

_____

Chromatography

_____

_____

_____

_____

_____

_____

_____

Distillation

_____

_____

_____

_____

_____

_____

_____

Lab Report: Rainbow Effect

Our Tools

_____   _____

_____   _____

Our Method

_____

_____

_____

_____

Our Outcome

What it looked like

Our Insight

_____

_____

_____

_____

Crystals

_____

_____

_____

_____

_____

_____

_____

_____

_____

_____

_____

_____

_____

Lab Report: Crystalline Shapes

Our Tools

_____   _____

_____   _____

Our Method

_____

_____

_____

_____

Our Outcome

What it looked like

Our Insight

_____

_____

_____

_____

Scientist Biography Questionnaire – Louis Pasteur

Title of Book

_____

When and where was Louis Pasteur born?

_____

_____

What was his major scientific contribution?

_____

_____

_____

_____

_____

List the events that surround his discovery.

_____

_____

_____

_____

_____

_____

_____

_____

_____

_____

_____

_____

List some other interesting events in the his life.

_____

_____

_____

_____

_____

_____

_____

_____

_____

_____

_____

Why do you think that it is important to learn about Louis Pasteur?

_____

_____

_____

_____

_____

_____

_____

Chemistry for the Grammar Stage

Acids and Bases Unit

Acids

Bases

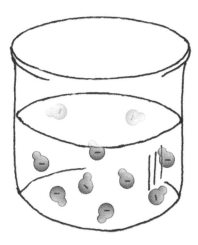

Acids

_____
_____
_____
_____
_____
_____
_____

_____
_____
_____
_____

Bases

_____
_____
_____
_____
_____
_____
_____
_____
_____
_____

Lab Report: Drinkable Acid

Our Tools

_____   _____

_____   _____

Our Method

_____

_____

_____

_____

_____

Our Outcome

	Color of solution
Lemonade	

_____

_____

_____

_____

Our Insight

_____

_____

_____

_____

14
13
12
11
10
9
8
7 — Neutral
6
5
4
3
2
1
0

Basic Range

Acidic Range

pH

_____

_____

_____

_____

_____

_____

_____

_____

_____

_____

_____

Indicator

_____

_____

_____

_____

_____

_____

_____

_____

_____

_____

_____

Neutral

Base

Acid

Lab Report: Acid-Base Testing

Our Tools

_____   _____

_____   _____

Our Method

_____

_____

_____

_____

Our Outcome

	Color Present
Vinegar	
Ammonia	

_____

_____

_____

Our Insight

_____

_____

_____

Neutral

Base   Acid

Neutralization

Base + Acid

_____
_____
_____
_____
_____
_____
_____

_____
_____
_____
_____

Salts

_____
_____
_____
_____
_____
_____

Na$^+$

Cl$^-$

_____
_____
_____

Lab Report: Neutralize It

Our Tools

_____ _____

_____ _____

Our Method

_____

_____

_____

_____

Our Outcome

What it looked like at the end

Our Insight

_____

_____

_____

_____

Base + Acid

Scientist Biography Questionnaire – Marie Curie

Title of Book

_____

When and where was Marie Curie born?

_____

_____

What was her major scientific contribution?

_____

_____

_____

_____

_____

List the events that surround her discovery.

_____

_____

_____

_____

_____

_____

_____

_____

_____

_____

_____

_____

List some other interesting events in the her life.

_____

_____

_____

_____

_____

_____

_____

_____

_____

_____

_____

Why do you think that it is important to learn about Marie Curie?

_____

_____

_____

_____

_____

_____

_____

_____

Chemistry for the Grammar Stage

Organic Chemistry Unit

Organic Compounds

_____

_____

_____

_____

_____

_____

Organic Acids

_____

_____

_____

_____

_____

_____

Detergents

_____

_____

_____

_____

_____

_____

DETERGENT

Ultra Clean!

Lab Report: Fat Test

Our Tools

_____   _____

_____   _____

Our Method

_____

_____

_____

_____

_____

Our Outcome

Type of Food:	Type of Food:	Type of Food:
Did it leave a stain? yes　　　no	Did it leave a stain? yes　　　no	Did it leave a stain? yes　　　no
Type of Food:	Type of Food:	Type of Food:
Did it leave a stain? yes　　　no	Did it leave a stain? yes　　　no	Did it leave a stain? yes　　　no

Our Insight

_____

_____

_____

Alcohols

_____

_____

_____

_____

_____

_____

_____

Fermentation

_____

_____

_____

_____

_____

_____

_____

Esters

_____

_____

_____

_____

_____

_____

_____

Lab Report: Spicy Perfume

Our Tools

_____   _____

_____   _____

Our Method

_____

_____

_____

_____

_____

Our Outcome

_____

_____

_____

_____

_____

Our Insight

_____

_____

_____

_____

_____

_____

Hydrocarbons

_____

_____

_____

_____

_____

_____

_____

_____

_____

_____

_____

_____

_____

_____

_____

_____

_____

_____

_____

_____

_____

_____

_____

Lab Report: Oily Clean-up

Our Tools

_____   _____

_____   _____

_____   _____

Our Method

_____

_____

_____

_____

Our Outcome

Material	How well did the material clean up the oil?
Spoon	
Cotton balls	
Polyester felt	

Our Insight

_____

_____

_____

Polymers

_____

_____

_____

_____

_____

_____

_____

_____

_____

_____

_____

Plastics

_____

_____

_____

_____

_____

_____

_____

_____

_____

_____

Lab Report: Kitchen Plastic

Our Tools

_____   _____

_____   _____

Our Method

> ### What it looked like

_____
_____
_____
_____
_____
_____
_____
_____
_____
_____

Our Outcome

_____

_____

_____

_____

Our Insight

_____

_____

_____

_____

Chemistry for the Grammar Stage

Glossary

Acid —

_____
_____
_____
_____

Air —

_____
_____
_____
_____

Alloy —

Pure Metal

_____
_____

Alloy

_____
_____

Atomic Mass —

| 15 |
| **P** |
| Phosphorus |
| 30.97 |

_____
_____
_____
_____

Atomic Number —

15
P
Phosphorus
30.97

_____

_____

_____

_____

Base —

_____

_____

_____

_____

Catalyst —

Reaction Pathway

normal path of a reaction

activation energy

activation energy when a catalyst has been introduced

reaction path with the addition of a catalyst

reactants

products

_____

_____

_____

_____

Chemical Bond —

O

H

H

shared electrons

_____

_____

_____

_____

Chemical Reaction —

_____

_____

$HCl + NaOH \longrightarrow H_2O + NaCl$ _____

_____

_____

Chemical Symbol —

| 15 |
| **P** |
| Phosphorus |
| 30.97 |

_____

_____

_____

_____

Chromatography —

_____

_____

_____

_____

Crystal —

_____

_____

_____

_____

Detergent —

_____
_____
_____
_____

Diffusion —

_____
_____
_____
_____

Electron —

_____
_____
_____
_____

Electron Shell —

_____
_____
_____
_____

Element —

13
Al
Aluminum
26.98

_____
_____
_____
_____

Enzyme —

_____
_____
_____
_____

Essential Element —

6
C
Carbon
12.01

_____
_____
_____
_____

Evaporation —

_____
_____
_____
_____

Fermentation —

_____
_____
_____
_____

Hard Water —

_____
_____
_____
_____

Indicator —

_____
_____
_____
_____

Inert —

_____
_____
_____
_____

110

Ion —

$H+$

_____
_____
_____
_____

Isotope —

| 17 |
| Cl $_{18n}$ |
| Chlorine |
| 35 |

| 17 |
| Cl $_{20n}$ |
| Chlorine |
| 37 |

_____
_____
_____
_____

Metal —

| 13 |
| Al |
| Aluminum |
| 26.98 |
| 31 |
| Ga |
| Gallium |
| 69.72 |

49	50
In	Sn
Indium	Tin
114.82	118.71

81	82	83
Tl	Pb	Bi
Thallium	Lead	Bismuth
204.38	207.2	208.98

_____
_____
_____
_____

Metalloid —

| 5 |
| B |
| Boron |
| 10.81 |

| 14 |
| Si |
| Silicon |
| 28.09 |

32	33
Ge	As
Germanium	Arsenic
72.61	74.92

51	52
Sb	Te
Antimony	Tellurium
121.8	127.6

| 84 |
| Po |
| Polonium |
| 209 |

_____
_____
_____
_____

Mixture —

_____
_____
_____
_____

Molecule —

_____
_____
_____
_____

Neutralization —

_____
_____
_____
_____

Neutron —

_____
_____
_____
_____

Nonmetal —

6	7	8
C	**N**	**O**
Carbon	Nitrogen	Oxygen
12.01	14.01	16
	15	16
	P	**S**
	Phosphorus	Sulfur
	30.97	32.07
		34
		Se
		Selenium
		78.96

_____

_____

_____

_____

Organic Compound —

_____

_____

_____

_____

Oxidation —

_____

_____

_____

_____

Periodic Table —

_____

_____

_____

_____

pH —

14
13
12
11
10
9
8
Basic Range
7 — Neutral
6
5
4
3
Acidic Range
2
1
0

_____

_____

_____

_____

Physical Change —

_____

_____

_____

_____

Polymer —

_____

_____

_____

_____

Proton —

_____

_____

_____

_____

Radioactive Decay —

_____
_____
_____
_____

Reactive —

_____
_____
_____
_____

Redox Reaction —

_____
_____
_____
_____

Refraction —

Light

Lens

_____
_____
_____
_____

Salt —

_____

_____

_____

_____

Solution —

_____

_____

_____

_____

States of Matter —

_____

_____

_____

_____

Sublimation —

_____

_____

_____

_____

Surface Tension —

_____

_____

_____

_____

Volume —

_____

_____

_____

_____

Chemistry for the Grammar Stage

Memory Work

Atoms and Molecules Unit

Atoms and Molecules

Atoms are the stuff that makes what we got,
Forming molecules found in your teapot.
Inside the atom are three little specks,
Subatomic particles kept in check.
At the center are neutrons and protons,
Spinning around in shells are electrons.
All three parts balanced in equality,
Gives the atom its own frivolity.
One or more atoms uniquely combine,
Creating a molecular design.
These molecules we can breathe, eat, and wear.
Meet them every day in water and air.

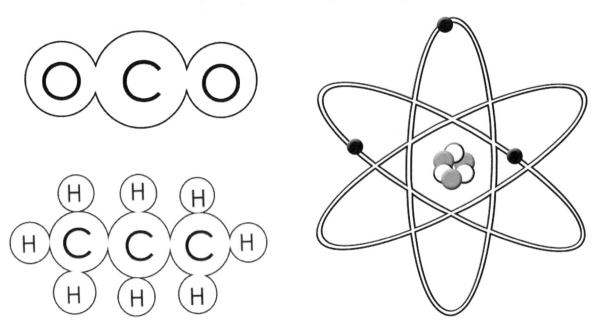

Periodic Table Unit

1 **H** Hydrogen 1.008	
3 **Li** Lithium 6.041	
11 **Na** Sodium 22.99	
19 **K** Potassium 39.1	
37 **Rb** Rubidium 85.47	
55 **Cs** Cesium 132.9	
87 **Fr** Francium 223	

The Periodic Table *(Author Unknown)*

Each element has a spot on the Periodic Table,
Whether metal or gas, radioactive or stable.
You can find out its number, its symbol, its weight,
And from its position, its physical state.

Elements lined up in columns and rows,
The reason for this order, as each chemist knows,
Is that atoms are made up of still smaller bits,
(Figuring this out tested scientists' wits!)

In the nucleus, protons and neutrons are found,
And a cloud of electrons is buzzing around.
First take one proton, put in its place;
Now you have hydrogen, the simplest case.

Add two neutrons and one more proton,
And suddenly, the hydrogen's gone!
Now you have helium, quite different stuff…
You get the picture; I've said enough.

These tiny particles: they're like building blocks
That make people and buildings, flowers and rocks.
They create all of the elements we find
In everyday things of every kind!

Physical Changes Unit

States of Matter

Three states of matter
Solid, liquid, gas
Molecules scatter
As heat enters mass

A solid is firm
Atoms locked in tight
No room found to squirm
We can take a bite

Liquid moves freely
Atoms flow and gush
Filling easily
Even helps you flush

A gas has no shape
Moves without control
It tries to escape
Out every hole

Chemical Changes Unit

Reactions

Atoms bump into each other in space
Bonding - connecting at a rapid pace
These compounds form in three main types of bonds
Different ways electrons correspond
In an ionic bond, one atom asks
The other gives electrons to the task
In a covalent bond the atoms share
Electrons joined in a happy pair
The metallic bond is a little strange
Electrons swirl in a constant exchange
This bonding happens in a reaction
Reactants to products - one cool action
As this tidy chemical change occurs
The mass stays the same, it only transfers
Exothermic reactions give off heat
Endothermic ones cool as atoms meet
Catalysts help by speeding up the pace
Redox is when electrons swap their place

$$HCl + NaOH \longrightarrow H_2O + NaCl$$

Mixtures Unit

Mixtures, Solutions, Oh My!

A mixture occurs when two things combine
Like in air, Kool-Aid, and a salty brine

A solid and liquid together mix
And form a solution - a mixture trick

One separates a mixture many ways
Filter, distill, evaporate - some stays

Through chromatography, people can see
Ink separate into colors with glee

Acids and Bases Unit

Acids and Bases

Acids dissolve in water to taste sour
Like the vinegar next to your flour

Bases break up into bitter compounds
Which can clean up stains left by coffee grounds

We measure their strength by the pH scale
Low for acids, High for base, tells the tale

But when we mix an acid and a base
Now, neutralization is what takes place

We see water and salt are left behind
A pH of 7 is what we find

Organic Chemistry Unit

<u>Organics</u>

Organic chem is the science of life
Carbon and hydrogen bond without strife

These compounds help keep our bodies
stable
But they can be made at the lab table

Alcohols have an OH group to boot
Esters make that sweet taste in gum or
fruit

Hydrocarbons are in gas and oil
Polymers create a long-chained coil

Chemistry for the Grammar Stage

Project Pictures

1
H
Hydrogen
1.008

3
Li
Lithium
6.041

11
Na
Sodium
22.99

19
K
Potassium
39.1

37
Rb
Rubidium
85.47

55
Cs
Cesium
132.9

87
Fr
Francium
223

4
Be
Beryllium
9.012

12
Mg
Magnesium
24.3

20
Ca
Calcium
40.08

38
Sr
Strontium
87.62

56
Ba
Barium
137.3

88
Ra
Radium
226

21	22	23	24	25	26	27	28	29	30
Sc	**Ti**	**V**	**Cr**	**Mn**	**Fe**	**Co**	**Ni**	**Cu**	**Zn**
Scandium	Titanium	Vanadium	Chromium	Manganese	Iron	Cobalt	Nickel	Copper	Zinc
44.96	47.87	50.94	52	54.94	55.85	58.93	58.69	63.55	65.39
39	40	41	42	43	44	45	46	47	48
Y	**Zr**	**Nb**	**Mo**	**Tc**	**Ru**	**Rh**	**Pd**	**Ag**	**Cd**
Yttrium	Zirconium	Niobium	Molybdenum	Technetium	Ruthenium	Rhodium	Palladium	Silver	Cadmium
88.91	91.22	92.91	95.94	98.91	101.07	102.91	106.42	107.87	112.41
* 71	72	73	74	75	76	77	78	79	80
Lu	**Hf**	**Ta**	**W**	**Re**	**Os**	**Ir**	**Pt**	**Au**	**Hg**
Lutetium	Hafnium	Tantalum	Tungsten	Rhenium	Osmium	Iridium	Platinum	Gold	Mercury
175	178.49	180.95	183.85	186.21	190.2	192.2	195.08	196.97	200.59
** 103	104	105	106	107	108	109	110	111	112
Lr	**Rf**	**Db**	**Sg**	**Bh**	**Hs**	**Mt**	**Ds**	**Rg**	**Cn**
Lawrencium	Rutherfordium	Dubnium	Seaborgium	Bohrium	Hassium	Meitnerium	Darmstadtium	Roentgenium	Copernicium
262	261.11	262.11	263.12	264.1	265.1	266	[271]	[272]	[277]

5
B
Boron
10.81

13
Al
Aluminum
26.98

31
Ga
Gallium
69.72

49
In
Indium
114.82

81
Tl
Thallium
204.38

113
Nh
Nihonium

6
C
Carbon
12.01

14
Si
Silicon
28.09

32
Ge
Germanium
72.61

50
Sn
Tin
118.71

82
Pb
Lead
207.2

114
Fl
Flerovium

7
N
Nitrogen
14.01

15
P
Phosphorus
30.97

33
As
Arsenic
74.92

51
Sb
Antimony
121.76

83
Bi
Bismuth
208.98

115
Mc
Moscovium

8
O
Oxygen
16

16
S
Sulfur
32.07

34
Se
Selenium
78.96

52
Te
Tellurium
127.6

84
Po
Polonium
208.98

116
Lv
Livermorium

9		2																70
F Fluorine 19		**He** Helium 4																**Yb** Ytterbium 173.04

17		10																69
Cl Chlorine 35.45		**Ne** Neon 20.18														102		**Tm** Thulium 168.93

35		18														**No** Nobelium 259.1		68
Br Bromine 79.9		**Ar** Argon 39.95													101			**Er** Erbium 167.26

53		36													**Md** Mendelevium 258.1			67
I Iodine 126.9		**Kr** Krypton 83.8												100				**Ho** Holmium 164.93

85		54												**Fm** Fermium 257.1				66
At Astatine 209.9		**Xe** Xenon 131.29											99					**Dy** Dysprosium 162.5

117		86											**Es** Einsteinium 252.08					65
Ts Tennessine		**Rn** Radon 222.02										98						**Tb** Terbium 158.93

		118										**Cf** Californium 251.08						64
		Og Oganesson									97							**Gd** Gadolinium 157.25

Actinide series:

89	90	91	92	93	94	95	96	97	98	99	100	101	102
Ac Actinium 227.03	**Th** Thorium 232.04	**Pa** Protactinium 231.04	**U** Uranium 238.03	**Np** Neptunium 237.04	**Pu** Plutonium 244.06	**Am** Americium 243.06	**Cm** Curium 247.07	**Bk** Berkelium 247.07	**Cf** Californium 251.08	**Es** Einsteinium 252.08	**Fm** Fermium 257.1	**Md** Mendelevium 258.1	**No** Nobelium 259.1

Lanthanide series:

57	58	59	60	61	62	63	64	65	66	67	68	69	70
La Lanthanum 138.91	**Ce** Cerium 140.12	**Pr** Praseodymium 14.91	**Nd** Neodymium 144.24	**Pm** Promethium 144.91	**Sm** Samarium 150.36	**Eu** Europium 151.96	**Gd** Gadolinium 157.25	**Tb** Terbium 158.93	**Dy** Dysprosium 162.5	**Ho** Holmium 164.93	**Er** Erbium 167.26	**Tm** Thulium 168.93	**Yb** Ytterbium 173.04

Chemistry for the Grammar Stage

Quizzes

Chemistry for the Grammar Stage Quizzes

Introduction

The quizzes found in this eBook are meant to coordinate with *Chemistry for the Grammar Stage*. The answers and schedule for using them are included in the *Chemistry for the Grammar Stage Teacher Guide*. You can use these quizzes to orally review the concepts learned or you can have the student complete one each week to test their retention of what they are learning with *Chemistry for the Grammar Stage*.

Table of Contents

Atoms and Molecules Week 1 Quiz

1. Match the following subatomic particles with their charge.

   Proton   Neutral

   Electron   Negative

   Neutron   Positive

2. An atom has _____ and _____ in a mass at

   the center with _____ spinning around the outside.

3. **True or False:** An isotope is an atom that has a different number of neutrons.

4. What is the most interesting thing you learned this week?

   _____

   _____

   _____

   _____

   _____

Atoms and Molecules Week 2 Quiz

1. Fill in the blanks with the number of electrons found in the shell.

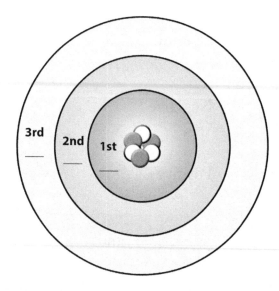

2. **True or False:** A molecule is always made up of only one element.

3. Polar molecules are (not charged / charged), while nonpolar molecules

   are (not charged / charged).

4. What is the most interesting thing you learned this week?

   _____

   _____

   _____

   _____

   _____

   _____

Atoms and Molecules Week 3 Quiz

1. Circle the two main gases that are found in air.

        oxygen   argon   nitrogen   chlorine

2. Oxygen is essential for _____.

        ice cream   life   rock formation

3. Animals take in (oxygen / carbon dioxide) and release (oxygen / carbon dioxide). Plants take in (oxygen / carbon dioxide) and release (oxygen / carbon dioxide).

5. What is the most interesting thing you learned this week?

_____

_____

_____

_____

_____

Atoms and Molecules Week 4 Quiz

1. _____ is the most abundant compound on the earth.

2. Hard water has (more / less) dissolved minerals. Soft water has (more / less) dissolved minerals.

3. **True or False:** Surface tension is caused by the attraction of the molecules found in a liquid.

4. What is the most interesting thing you learned this week?

_____

_____

_____

_____

_____

_____

1. Fill in the blanks with atomic number, atomic mass, and chemical symbol.

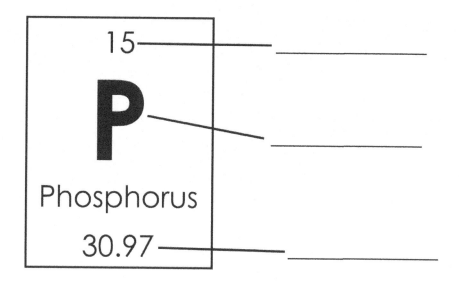

2. **True or False:** The periodic table was first designed by Dmitri Mendeleev.

3. **True or False:** An element is made up of multiple different atoms.

4. What is the most interesting thing you learned this week?

_____

_____

_____

_____

_____

_____

Periodic Table Week 2 Quiz

1. **True or False:** The alkali metals are a very reactive group.

2. Hydrogen exists as a _____ on Earth.

3. Circle all the characteristics of sodium.

     found in lots of common compounds   very reactive

     blue gas   light gray metal   very hard

4. What is the most interesting thing you learned this week?

   _____

   _____

   _____

1	_____
H	_____
Hydrogen	_____
1.008	

Periodic Table Week 3 Quiz

1. Circle all the characteristics of alkaline earth metals.

     soft metals   often bonded to oxygen   react easily

2. **True or False:** Magnesium is a gas that burns with a bright purple-blue light.

3. Name two places that you can find calcium-containing compounds.

   _____

   _____

4. What is the most interesting thing you learned this week?

   _____

   _____

   _____

   _____

   _____

   _____

| 12 |
| Mg |
| Magnesium |
| 24.3 |

Periodic Table Week 4 Quiz

1. The amazing ability of transition metals is that they can _____

   with a variety of other elements to form alloys.

2. **True or False:** Iron can be found in the core of the Earth.

3. Copper metal can be found in which type of US coins?

   Dimes   Pennies   Quarters

4. What is the most interesting thing you learned this week?

   _____

   _____

   _____

   _____

   _____

   _____

29

Cu

Copper
63.55

1. **True or False:** Boron is the only element in the boron elements groups that is

   different than the rest.

2. **True or False:** Boron is the only metal in the group of nonmetal boron

   elements.

3. Aluminum is (a rare / an abundant) element on the Earth.

4. What is the most interesting thing you learned this week?

   _____

   _____

   _____

   _____

   _____

   _____

| 13 |
| Al |
| Aluminum |
| 26.98 |

Periodic Table Week 6 Quiz

1. The carbon elements group contains: (Circle all that apply.)

    metals   nonmetals   neither

2. Why is carbon so important to us?

    _____

    _____

    _____

3. **True or False:** Tin cans are made from solid tin with no other metals.

4. What is the most interesting thing you learned this week?

    _____

    _____

6

C

Carbon

12.01

_____

_____

_____

_____

Periodic Table Week 7 Quiz

1. **True or False:** The nitrogen elements have a mish-mash collection of properties.

2. Nitrogen makes up _____ of the air on Earth.

      20 %   50 %   80 %

3. Circle all of the characteristics of phosphorus.

      appears in red, black, and white   is essential to life

      found in fertilizer   is a liquid at room temperature

4. What is the most interesting thing you learned this week?

_____

_____

_____

_____

_____

_____

_____

_____

7

N

Nitrogen

14.01

Periodic Table Week 8 Quiz

1. The oxygen elements are (not important   /   important   ) to life and

   industry.

2. Why is oxygen so important to us?

   _____

   _____

   _____

3. **True or False:** Sulfur is a pale yellow solid that smells like rotten eggs.

4. What is the most interesting thing you learned this week?

   _____

   _____

   _____

   _____

   _____

   _____

   _____

8

O

Oxygen

15.999

Periodic Table Week 9 Quiz

1. **True or False:** The elements in the halogens group are not very reactive.

2. Circle all of the places you can find fluorine compounds.

    drinking water   solid rocks

                        Teflon coatings

3. **True or False:** Iodine is added to table salt.

4. What is the most interesting thing you learned this week?

    _____

    _____

    _____

    _____

    _____

    _____

    _____

53
I
Iodine
126.9

1. The noble gases are the (most / least) reactive elements in the periodic table.

2. **True or False:** Helium is heavier than air.

3. When Neon comes in contact with electrical energy, it is _____.

    sluggish   excited   unchanged

4. What is the most interesting thing you learned this week?

    _____

    _____

    _____

    _____

    _____

    _____

    _____

| 10 |
| Ne |
| Neon |
| 20.18 |

Periodic Table Week 11 Quiz

1. **True or False:** Many of the elements in lanthanide group are naturally occurring.

2. Lanthanum is often used in _____.

   car doors   good lens   bookcases

3. Neodymium is (not   /   very   ) magnetic.

4. What is the most interesting thing you learned this week?

   _____

   _____

   _____

   _____

   _____

   _____

   _____

57
La
Lanthanum
138.91

Periodic Table Week 12 Quiz

1. **True or False:** Many of the elements in the actinide group are   radioactive.

2. In radioactive decay, an atom loses particles until it becomes a more

   _____.

3. Uranium is often used in _____.

   generating power   purifying water   cleaning up spills

4. What is the most interesting thing you learned this week?

   _____

   _____

   _____

| 92 |
| **U** |
| Uranium |
| 238.03 |

   _____

   _____

   _____

   _____

   _____

Physical Changes Week 1 Quiz

1. Match the state of matter.

   Solid _____   A. Has no fixed shape or volume.

   Liquid _____   B. Has a fixed shape and volume.

   Gas _____   C. Has a fixed volume, but not a fixed shape.

2. **True or False:** Volume is the amount of space occupied by matter.

3. **True or False:** The molecules in a gas have less energy than the molecules in a solid.

4. What is the most interesting thing you learned this week?

_____

_____

_____

_____

_____

_____

Physical Changes Week 2 Quiz

1. When a solid _____, it turns into a liquid.

   When a liquid _____, it turns into a gas.

   melts   boils   condenses

2. When a liquid _____, it turns into a solid.

   When a liquid _____, it turns into a gas.

   condenses   freezes   evaporates

3. What is the most interesting thing you learned this week?

   _____

   _____

   _____

                    _____

                    _____

                    _____

Solid

Liquid

Gas

Physical Changes Week 3 Quiz

1. Liquids can change _____, but the _____ remains the same.

    volume   shape   color

2. **True or False:** The cooler a liquid gets, the quicker it evaporates.

3. **True or False:** Surface tension is the result of the molecules in a liquid being attracted to each other.

4. What is the most interesting thing you learned this week?

    _____

    _____

    _____

    _____

    _____

    _____

Physical Changes Week 4 Quiz

1. **True or False:** Brownian motion is the random motion of molecules within a liquid or gas.

2. In diffusion, molecules move from an area of (high   /   low   ) concentration to an area of (high   /   low   ) concentration.

3. _____ is the push that gas molecules exert on a container.

    volume   pressure   temperature

4. What is the most interesting thing you learned this week?

    _____

    _____

    _____

                              _____

                              _____

                              _____

Chemical Changes Week 1 Quiz

1. In _____ bonding an electron is gained or lost.

   ionic   covalent   metallic

2. In _____ bonding electrons are free to travel within a lattice.

   ionic   covalent   metallic

3. In _____ bonding an electron is shared between two atoms.

   ionic   covalent   metallic

4. What is the most interesting thing you learned this week?

   _____

   _____

   _____

   _____

   _____

   _____

shared electrons

Chemical Changes Week 2 Quiz

1. A chemical reaction begins with (reactants / products) and ends with (reactants / products).

2. The Law of Conservation of Mass says that amount of matter in a chemical reaction_____.

       increases   stays the same   decreases

3. **True or False:** A mole is the unit that chemists use to measure substances.

4. What is the most interesting thing you learned this week?

_____

_____

_____

           _____

           _____

           _____

Chemical Changes Week 3 Quiz

1. A reaction that produces heat is called an _____ reaction. A

   reaction that takes in heat is called an _____ reaction.

          endothermic   activated   exothermic

2. **True or False:** A catalyst can only slow down a reaction.

3. A catalyst that speeds up a reaction in a living thing is called an _____.

          quickinator   enzyme   protein

4. What is the most interesting thing you learned this week?

   _____

   _____

   _____

   _____

   _____

   _____

Chemical Changes Week 4 Quiz

1. **True or False:** An oxidation or reduction, a.k.a. redox, reaction involves the transfer of electrons.

2. Combustion is an example of a(n) _____ reaction.

   oxidation   reduction

3. Photosynthesis is an example of a(n) _____ reaction.

   oxidation   reduction

4. What is the most interesting thing you learned this week?

   _____

   _____

   _____

                        _____

                        _____

                        _____

Mixtures Week 1 Quiz

1. **True or False:** A mixture contains a combination a two or more elements.

2. A solution is formed when a _____ is dissolved in a liquid.

       gas   liquid   solid

3. When two liquids mix easily, they are called (immiscible / miscible).

   When two liquids do not mix easily, they are called (immiscible / miscible).

4. What is the most interesting thing you learned this week?

   _____

   _____

   _____

   _____

   _____

Mixtures Week 2 Quiz

1. Filtration is a method of separating _____.

    liquids from gases   solids from liquids   solids from gases

2. **True or False:** You can not use chromatography to determine what colors are in

    an ink pen.

3. Distillation is a method of separating two or more _____.

    solids   liquids   gases

4. What is the most interesting thing you learned this week?

    _____

    _____

    _____

                                        _____

                                        _____

                                        _____

Mixtures Week 3 Quiz

1. Crystals form as a solution _____.

   Cools off   Heats up

2. **True or False:** A crystal is a solid with a definite geometric shape.

3. **True or False:** Crystals only have rounded edges and surfaces.

4. What is the most interesting thing you learned this week?

   _____

   _____

   _____

   _____

   _____

   _____

Mixtures Week 4 Quiz

1. What have you learned about Louis Pasteur this week?

_____

_____

_____

_____

_____

_____

_____

_____

_____

Acids and Bases Week 1 Quiz

1. **True or False:** An acid dissolves in water and can taste sour.

2. Some common acids are _____.

      vinegar   water   ammonia   lemon juice

2. **True or False:** An base dissolves in water and can taste sour.

3. Some common acids are _____.

      water   baking soda   ammonia   lemon juice

4. What is the most interesting thing you learned this week?

_____

_____

_____

_____

_____

Acids and Bases Week 2 Quiz

1. pH stands for _____.

   potential of hydrology   power of hydrogren

2. Label the following pH's with what they represent - acid, base, or neutral.

   pH 2 _____

   pH 7 _____

   pH 10 _____

3. **True or False:** An indicator is a substance that changes color in the presence of an acid or a base.

4. What is the most interesting thing you learned this week?

   Neutral

   Base   Acid

   _____
   _____
   _____
   _____
   _____

Acids and Bases Week 3 Quiz

1. When you mix an acid and a base, you get _____ and

   a _____.

2. **True or False:** A salt is formed when you mix an acid and a base.

3. A salt dissolves in water to form _____.

   bases   ions   acids

4. What is the most interesting thing you learned this week?

   _____

   _____

   _____

   _____

   _____

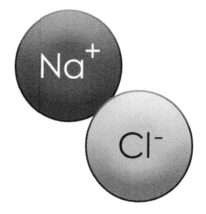

Acids and Bases Week 4 Quiz

1. What have you learned about Marie Curie this week?

_____

_____

_____

_____

_____

_____

_____

_____

Organic Chemistry Week 1 Quiz

1. All organic compounds have _____.

2. **True or False:** Organic acids behave the same as other acids.

3. A _____ is a substance that allows water to remove dirt.

   acids   detergents   esters

4. What is the most interesting thing you learned this week?

   _____

   _____

   _____

   _____

   _____

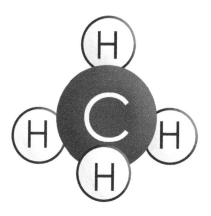

Organic Chemistry Week 2 Quiz

1. Circle the elements below that are found in alcohols.

   Carbon   Hydrogen   Iron   Oxygen

2. **True or False:** Fermentation is a chemical reaction that produces an organic acid.

3. Esters are responsible for the _____ in flowers, fruit, and perfume.

   touch   taste   smell

4. What is the most interesting thing you learned this week?

   _____

   _____

   _____

   _____

   _____

   _____

Organic Chemistry Week 3 Quiz

1. **True or False:** Crude oil can be separated through distillation to make a lot of useful hydrocarbon compounds.

2. Circle the following chemicals that are hydrocarbons.

   gas   oil   kerosene

        candle wax   lubricants

3. Crude oil is separated by a process called _____.

   pulling   fractional distillation   blast separation

4. What is the most interesting thing you learned this week?

   _____

   _____

   _____

   _____

   _____

   _____

Organic Chemistry Week 4 Quiz

1. Polymers are made up of _____ chains of molecules.

     short   long

2. **True or False:** Polymerization is the process of joining up molecules to make polymers.

3. Synthetic polymers and plastics are made by _____.

     man   nature

4. What is the most interesting thing you learned this week?

   _____

   _____

   _____

   _____

   _____

   _____

Made in the USA
Middletown, DE
27 June 2021